The flying squirrel and other stories from the woodlands

The flying squirrel and other stories from the woodlands

Selected by Ruth Spriggs

Illustrated by Cliff Wright

Peter Lowe

THE AUTHORS

Frances Ball: pages 7,11,35,41,50,56
Susan Hazeldine: page 23
Celia Maier: pages 14,26,47,60
Felicity Marsh: pages 17,20,29,32,44,53
Laurence Smith: page 38

Consultant zoologist: Celia Maier

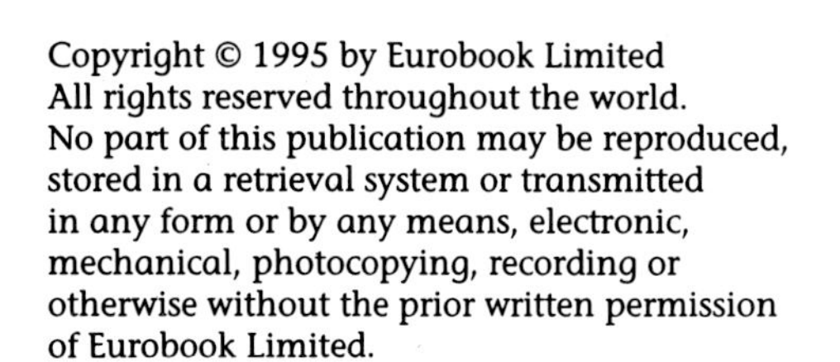

ISBN 0 85654 064 1

Printed in Italy by Arti Grafiche Ricordi.

Contents

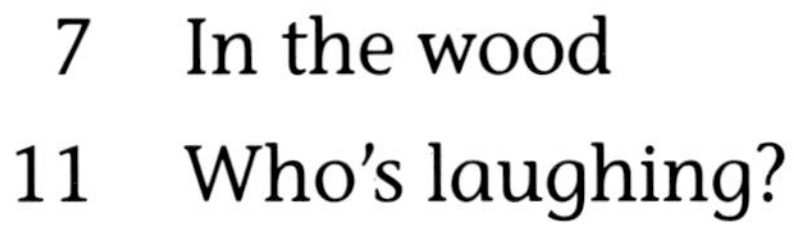

7 In the wood
11 Who's laughing?
14 The golden shadow
17 A very special meal
20 The cuckoo's summer
23 Night visitors
26 A web in the bracken
29 A place to sleep
32 The owl's windy night
35 The hunter
38 The flying squirrel
41 Fur and feathers
44 A new home for the fox
47 The woodmouse's secret
50 Winter's on the way
53 New arrivals
56 Just a meal of corn
60 The wood at night
64 Something to think about

In the wood

A few drops of rain fell on to the wood. They washed the leaves and fell into the shallow water of the lake. Two children ran along the path that wound between the trees at the lake edge, hurrying home to the village. The sun was setting, and darkness would come quickly as more clouds hid the last of the light.

A weasel looked out of her burrow below the elder tree, sniffed the air, then set off in search of supper. Her long narrow body moved easily between the stalks and roots, the tip of of her tail finally disappearing below the old stone wall that edged one side of the wood. Its cracks and crevices provided homes for mice and voles. It was a favourite hunting place.

The wind grew stronger, driving the rain against the trees, and moving the branches from side to side. High up in the leaves, the rooks' nests swayed about. It was past breeding time but birds still roosted there at night.

Below them, a tattered woodmouse looked for a new home. He had been caught last night by an owl, but dropped when the owl was suddenly dazzled by the lights of a car turning into the village. He had fallen to safety in a pile of bracken, where he spent the day regaining his strength. But the weasel had now passed and the bracken was moving about in the wind. He needed a home.

Thunder rumbled beyond the hill, followed by a flash of lightning. Some of the animals below ground heard the heavy rain falling at the entrances to their homes. The badgers waited in their sett below the oak tree. A cold wind was blowing down the main tunnel. Tomorrow would be a hungry day unless they searched for food tonight.

Leaves shook loose from the trees, and a sudden gust of wind broke the tall stems of the foxgloves. The weasel returned. She was not hungry any more but her long body looked thinner than ever where the wet fur clung to her skin.

The wind slackened and it seemed as if the storm had passed. Then more lightning streaked the sky and the thunder crashed overhead. A tearing noise came from the hollow oak near the lake. The lightning had struck its last large branch, and a loud crack sounded as it finally broke from the trunk. It fell into the lake, splashing the ducks sheltering on the small island. If the branch made a bridge across the water, they would be in danger from foxes. The water was their protection.

The rain continued all the night. Then a final heavy shower marked the passing of the storm. The sky would be clear when the daytime animals began to stir.

The tattered woodmouse had found a new home in an empty hole. The hole's last owner, probably a vole, had abandoned it. Perhaps it had set off to look for food and ended up as a meal for a larger animal. The woodmouse had survived dangers from the owl and weasel. Would he be so lucky again?

The jays were about early, shrieking through the dripping trees, looking for all the acorns shaken free during the night. The ducks paddled around the lake, unable to do anything about the fallen branch. Other, smaller branches had fallen in other parts of the wood. They would make good homes for beetles and spiders, centipedes and woodlice.

As the day continued, the wood began to return to normal. The daily search for food and bedding, materials for nests and repairs, tidied the night's damage. Only the fallen branches and snapped foxgloves showed clearly what had

happened. And a few small creatures had been stranded by sudden streams and puddles.

Some of the grey squirrels had left their dreys to collect food, and one young mole appeared before hurrying back to the comfort of his dry underground home. The storm had made little difference to the moles.

When the sun grew stronger, a man walked his dog through the wood, following the path that led from the village to the fields. Deep in thought, he didn't notice the busy squirrels above him or the shrews scattering as his dog played in the leaves. On his way back, he noticed the damaged tree by the lake but that was all. The tattered woodmouse ventured out to find some food. He was cold and hungry. He found some rather battered berries, then returned to his borrowed home, curling up tightly well away from the entrance.

Later in the day, a girl and her mother visited the wood. They brought bread for the ducks. They walked quietly through the leaves but they still made enough noise to warn the animals that more humans were about. A hedgehog curled up in his pile of leaves after they had caught a glimpse of him, and the squirrels watched from above.

The girl and her mother visited the wood each week. They knew how many ducklings had hatched, and how many had survived. One had been lost but they never found out what had happened to him. Today, they counted the ducks again. None had been lost in the night.

As they began throwing the bread, the old carp who patrolled the lake swam round. His usual route had been disturbed by the fallen branch but he would get used to it. It was a clear, bright evening as the girl and her mother returned home. The daytime animals would gain a little time before their neighbours who came out at night appeared. The tattered woodmouse had eaten well. He slept, safe for now.

Who's laughing?

The two woodpeckers flew between the rows of larch trees. Their strange calls "Gua, gua,gua" sounded like laughter, but they were not laughing: they were frightened. Early that morning two men had come to the wood looking at the trees, then painting rings round some of them. They had painted the woodpeckers' tree.

The birds had just completed their new nest, carefully boring a neat entrance hole, then a comfortable chamber. They had been on a nearby branch, searching for grubs, when the men arrived. They had watched them, and had seen them leave. Everything had returned to normal.

But now they could hear a noise. It was a roaring, grinding noise, followed by clanking and banging. And it was coming nearer.

They flew around their tree, calling loudly. "Gua, gua, gua" echoed through the trees. Below them, the men were looking at the rough path and the position of the tree. The birds had chosen a damaged tree for their home, and now it was going to be cut down. They would have to make another nest.

The men hadn't noticed the nest high above them, but they had heard the birds. "Listen to them," one said. "I reckon they're laughing at us."

"It's probably the ones that lived in that telegraph pole before the gale," the other replied.

Now the *men* laughed – but they hadn't laughed at the time. The woodpeckers knew nothing of the trouble they had caused. Last year they had made their nest in a telegraph pole beside the lane. The large chamber they had drilled had weakened the pole. When they moved on, rain filled the hole, rotting the sides. The pole snapped in a gale, bringing down the phone lines.

Now it was the woodpeckers' turn to be disturbed! The large, noisy machine arrived, and screeched through the wood of the trunk. As the tree crashed to the ground, twigs and leaves flew into the air, and the homes of many other creatures were also damaged. Those that liked the shade below the trees suddenly found themselves in warm sunlight. The tree was chained up and taken away.

At first the homeless woodpeckers just flew around, keeping away from the men and the noisy machine. Their green backs and red crowns shone brightly against the clear blue sky. They did not want to move far. The wood was usually a good place for woodpeckers. It was home to many wood ants (good woodpecker food) and across the fields were oak trees which provided a tasty supply of acorns.

They started to look for a suitable tree, then followed the line of a hedge, a little way beyond the wood. An old oak tree marked the corner of a field. It was a healthy tree but it had a deep rot hole which would give the woodpeckers a useful start to their drilling.

First they searched under the loose fragments of bark for something to eat, wriggling their long tongues into all the hidden holes. They found woodlice there and beetle larvae and centipedes. Then they began the noisy task of drilling out their new home. Most of the wood chippings flew through the air but they left some in the bottom of the chamber. It was warmer like that.

Before long they would need the chamber for their eggs, so they worked quickly, disturbed only by the occasional sound of a tractor in the field. But the farmer left the tree and its birds alone.

During May six young woodpeckers forced their way out of their white eggshells. Within a few days, they were making more noise than their parents! At first, their feathers were light and very spotted. But gradually they came to look more like the older birds. When they left the nest, the parents still fed them for a while, until it was clear that they could look after themselves. Unless they were attacked by starlings (always a danger to young woodpeckers) they would be safe in their new home. Soon, their laughing calls were a familiar sound in the field.

All these woodpeckers would want their own homes as the summer passed. They would be looking at trees, telegraph poles, sometimes the large wooden beams high up in houses. If *you* have heard a lot of laughter and some noisy drilling, maybe there is another family of woodpeckers living somewhere nearby.

The golden shadow

The wood rose green and solid into the sky. The line of trees which made up its edge was a patchwork of different shapes and shades of green. The horse chestnut tree was the most fully clothed, with its heavy, dark leaves completely hiding the trunk and branches. From top to bottom its cone of green was decorated with spikes of flowers, like an old-fashioned Christmas tree. Next to the chestnut was a tall oak. Its leaves were still small and soft, pale green tinged with rose-gold and the tree's branches were not yet hidden. Other shades and shapes made up the wood: the pale, delicate birch with its small quivering leaves, the silvery willow, and the bright emerald beech.

As evening came the many different colours and details of the trees seemed to melt into each other. Darkness filled the wood. On the inky black woodland floor the night was filled with soft rustling sounds and shining eyes.

Towards the end of the night, just as a grey light was filling the eastern sky, a small, silent black shadow could be seen speeding over the tree tops. As the sky grew brighter, the shadow's long narrow wings carried it down into the depths of the wood, gliding and turning between the trees until it came to a tall, ancient beech tree. The shadow landed high on the trunk and the wings were quickly folded away. Long thumbs with sharp little hooked claws helped the shadow climb a short distance up the trunk to where a branch had long ago broken off, leaving a hole in its place. The shadow disappeared into the hole.

When the light once again began to fade, a soft chattering and scrabbling started up in the hole in the tree.

A head, followed by a sleek furry body, peeped out to see whether the harsh bright sun had finally disappeared. It was a glossy, chestnut-gold noctule bat. She was large compared to the other bats which flew in the wood, but still no bigger than a mouse when her long narrow wings were folded by her sides. The soft light of dusk was darkening over the wood: it was time for her to fly. She leaned forward from the edge of the hole, spread her wings and dropped from the trunk. The steep dive took her almost to the ground before she straightened out and, with a steady rapid flight, rose into the air again until she was skirting the tops of the trees. Not far behind her came another of her kind, and then another. Each bat dropped from the tree, rose again and then sped away over the wood.

The old beech tree was where the golden noctule first met her companions each spring. Joined by others, they spent a week or two there before moving on. As the summer passed they moved from tree to tree—to the deep crack in the ash tree by the clearing, then to a hole in the stout branch of the tall oak. By mid-June they arrived at the dead beech at the edge of the clearing. By this time there were usually about twenty noctules living together, some of whom had known each other for years—mothers and daughters, sisters and aunts. The tree was tall and bare, and it was several years since it had last shown new leaves in the spring. The bats stayed in an old woodpecker's hole high in the bare trunk. Having no leaves to shade it, the trunk grew warm in the sunshine each day, which suited the roosting bats very well.

Around midnight, following a long hot day in late June, the sleek golden shadow of the bat returned to the roost in the beech tree. She had spent the early part of the night hunting over a nearby meadow. She had flown high over the field, shouting into the dark to pick up echoes which bounced off the flying insects of the night. Large winged beetles were her favourite, and she would dive and chase and catch them on the wing as they buzzed below her. Tonight the hunting was more tiring than usual. She felt heavy and her long narrow wings were working harder than ever. When she was safely back in the tree, she groomed her sleek fur, cleaned her wings and then quietly edged a little away from the other bats who had now returned to rest. Before dawn, the others all left again to hunt for an hour or so over the pond at the bottom of the wood, but she stayed alone in the tree. When the other bats returned with the first light of dawn, there was a new arrival in the roost. The bat was chattering quietly and gently nuzzling her head under her wing. Hidden beneath the black cloak, held tight against her side, was her new-born baby.

A very special meal

One night late in June, as darkness fell in the wood, a badger stuck his head out of his hole and sniffed at the light wind that was blowing his way. He was ready to go back underground into the tunnels and chambers of his sett and wait if he smelled danger. Or he could come out at another hole altogether. But there was nothing to worry him on the breeze. Nor could he hear any crackle or rustle in the undergrowth.

He did not see anything suspicious either, but then badgers do not have good eyesight. Satisfied that all was well, he pushed through the tall grasses and brambles that hid each entrance to his sett.

It was a lovely warm night, and the stars were piercingly bright points of white in the black sky. When the badger glanced up at the moon it was hanging like a great yellow ball above the trees. He sat down to scratch, as all badgers do when they leave their sett. Then off he went, pad, pad, ambling down one of his paths between the trees, and on to the river, sniffing the air as he went to find out who else was about in the wood that night.

He went quite slowly because he was not afraid of many things. He was a strong animal and the thick hairs on his back could stand on end. They made him look big and fierce enough to stop most other creatures even thinking of attacking him. What was more, the claws he used for digging were just as useful in a fight and so was his tough skin and his hard head. So on he went, afraid of nothing. Pad, pad, pad, his back foot trod just where the front one had been until he reached the river. When he had had a drink, he sniffed the damp air that carried scents so well.

What was that mingling with all the other smells of the night? Could it be? Yes, it had to be: he could smell honey!

Honey! Now there are a lot of things that badgers eat – most of all they eat earthworms, and then they eat slugs and grubs and beetles too, and berries and beechnuts, a little corn maybe and, well, a hundred and one things – but they *do* like honey.

The honey that he could smell that night had been made by bees living in the hollow trunk of a tree. It had once stood on the river's edge and had fallen down two summers before. Now it was quite hidden from view, but that did not stop the badger from smelling the honey. He headed straight for it, pushing under brambles, over roots and through goosegrass to reach it.

The bees, of course, had made their honey for themselves, not for badgers, and when this badger broke into their nest they immediately tried to protect the honey and the nest by stinging him. He pushed his long, strong, claws right into the rotten wood, and with the big paws that are so useful for digging homes in the ground he ripped great pieces off. The bees flew round and round, buzzing and darting in to sting him as often as they could. Very few of them could pass through his thick fur and those that did found it hard to sting his tough skin. Soon his nose was sticky and his paws were sticky. One or two of the bees stung his nose and made him shake his head a little, but none of them bothered him very much, and in fact he ate a few of them too. Anyway, nothing they did stopped him eating his fill of the honey, and when – after he had licked his nose and paws – he finally padded off, he left the bees flying round and round in angry circles.

He returned to the wood by another of his family's paths, calling in at a few other setts, as he did most nights. On the way he paused to eat a slug here and a beetle there, but nothing else tasted as good to him as the honey had. He stopped with the other badgers for a while. He watched the cubs sliding down the heap of earth and old leaves they had found to play on, and paused to scratch the elder trees nearby and sharpen his claws.

Exactly how he spent the night was a mystery wrapped in the darkness. Badgers had lived in that part of the wood for hundreds of years. They had made paths in all directions and nothing is easier for them than to slip unnoticed through the dark. When the sun was ready to rise and the sky was turning from dark to light, he finally ambled back to his sett to rest. He paused when he reached the patch of grass that hid his hole and stretched his tongue to the far end of his whiskers. There, at the very tip, was the last little bit of honey.

The cuckoo's summer

High in the April air a tired cuckoo beat her wings in short, fast flaps. She was looking down at a small wood that lay on the side of a low hill. At the bottom of the hill, where the trees thinned out, a shallow stream bubbled its way over its stony bed, curving this way and that on its way to a narrow bridge. On the other side of the stream a herd of black and white cows was grazing. And directly below, halfway down the field, there was an old stone barn. The cuckoo shivered a little and looked for somewhere to land. In the early morning the fields beneath her were still damp and the hedgerows dripped quietly. The cuckoo raised her tail, drooped her wings, and landed on a fencepost, ruffling her feathers. Her long flight from Africa was over: she had found the place where she was born.

Soon she felt stronger. She stretched her wings and looked around. In a few weeks she would lay her eggs and in the late summer there would be more young cuckoos flying south for the winter.

The young cuckoos would need nests and food. At this time of the year all the other birds were building their nests. The cuckoo noticed a large rook with a beakful of straw. It made its way to a tall tree in the wood and busied itself at an untidy looking nest. The cuckoo ruffled her feathers again. There was no need for her to spend her spring building a nest and her summer looking after a brood of hungry chicks. She stretched her throat and sang.

As the weeks passed the weather grew warmer. The trees blossomed and became green. Flowers grew in the hedgerows and young animals wobbled their way around meadows on shaky legs that grew stronger and longer every day. From all the hidden, leafy places came the sound of cuckoos calling. The birds who had nests to build or repair collected moss and grass and twigs and wool, but not the cuckoos. Cuckoos never build nests.

Each day, however, our cuckoo was busy spying out other birds' nests. She looked for insect-eating birds who would bring her chicks the right kind of food. For cuckoos never feed their own chicks. And she was searching for the kind of nest she had been reared in herself. She saw where the robins and dunnocks lived and where the reed warblers and meadow pipits laid their eggs, but their nests were not right for her. The small birds tried to drive her away if they saw her. But for most of the time, she was unseen.

The day came when the cuckoo was ready to lay her first egg. From a perch in an old oak tree she watched the ivy on the empty barn. She had seen a pair of wagtails flying in and out of there several times. The slim branch swayed and creaked as she waited for them to leave. As soon as they had both flown off she raced down to their nest. It was the kind she needed. After looking round quickly, she settled on the nest and in a few moments laid her first egg.

Some cuckoos, especially those that have hatched in the nests of meadow pipits or reed warblers, can match eggs almost perfectly: they lay white eggs with brownish spots in meadow pipits' nests on the ground, greenish eggs in reed warblers' nests by ponds and streams. Our cuckoo's egg did not match the ones in the nest but the wagtails would not notice. They would feed and care for her chick as a pair of wagtails had once cared for her. She picked up one of the wagtails' eggs to make more room for her own larger one and flew off with it before they came back.

Over the next few days, the cuckoo watched and waited for other wagtails to leave their nests. One by one she laid her eggs. Each was in a different nest: one large, hungry cuckoo chick was quite enough for a pair of small birds to care for.

At last she had only one more egg to lay. But she had already used all the wagtail nests she knew. All day she searched for a home for her last chick. Suddenly she saw a flash of black and white. There was a wagtail's nest in the honeysuckle by the bridge. How could she have missed it? Minutes later her last egg was laid and she flew off.

In each nest a cuckoo chick hatched and grew . . . and grew . . . and grew. Soon they were much bigger than the small birds that worked so hard to feed them. The young cuckoos that flew south for the winter never knew who their real mother was. But the wagtails were good parents and next spring one female cuckoo would come back to look for their nest in the honeysuckle by the bridge.

Night visitors

It is growing dark in the forest. The light seems to be draining away quite quickly and it is difficult to see. From the scuttlings and munchings going on all round it is obvious that many creatures are still very much awake. Actually, even if you do not see very well in the dark at first, when your eyes get used to the dimness it is possible to pick out shapes and movements. There, to the right, is the rusting shed which the gamekeeper built out of corrugated iron. To the left is an old hornbeam tree, called the white tree because its white trunk shines out as a landmark in the forest. Between the shed and the white tree is something new, a wide, shadowy something that was not there a few hours before. Suddenly, an ear flicks: it's not one something but eight.

Out of the gloom gazes a small herd of fallow deer, standing so still that only an itchy ear shows where they are. Now it is possible to make out their shapes, their spotted coats grey in the dim light, their spreading antlers, their staring eyes. Still they do not move, but keep their ground. Then, at an invisible signal from their leader, they all turn to the left and bound away through the bushes, pushing aside anything in their way.

The forest returns to its quiet rustlings, although a tawny owl some way away hoo hoots from its tree – disturbed by the disappearing deer.

These fallow deer were half wild and half tame – as tame as such timid animals could be. Well over a hundred years ago their great-great-great-grandparents escaped over a crumbling park wall. Their owner, who did not want to hunt or eat them anyway, was quite pleased. When he caught sight of them peacefully wandering among the old chestnuts he even forgave them for eating the new leaves and twigs of the young trees.

Night was the time when they were most active and now they were heading through the black trees towards their latest feeding place. Keeping together and running gently, they emerged from the trees just in time to see the last daylight seep away over the far hill. The deer slowed to a walk, lowered their heads and began to nibble the soft meadow grass. Darkness was everywhere.

Far away a car was making its way quietly up one of the tracks towards the forest. Its headlights were only on dimly: the men inside did not want anyone to see them. And although they were driving towards the deer, it was not deer they were after but badgers. In the back of the car were two bull terriers, their noses covered in scars. They had been set to fight badgers before!

The car stopped before they reached the trees and the men got out and unloaded spades and ropes from the boot. They checked which way the wind was blowing. The animals must not smell them coming. And they kept the terriers on their leads as they walked towards the trees. They did not want the badgers to get away without a fight.

They were near the first trees when they caught sight of the grazing deer.

"Look at that," whispered one of the men. "I've always fancied venison. I hear it's good meat."

"Don't," said the other, who had seen a video of Bambi and did not like the idea of hurting one of his relations. But the first man was already bending some wire into a snare. He fixed it to a strong root that was sticking out of the ground. "This should catch one of them, no trouble. Then we can finish it off easily."

He wiped the soil from his hands onto his trousers. The two men crept quietly forward, still holding the dogs.

The leader of the deer lifted his head with its impressive antlers. The bitter smell of man, his only enemy, was in his nostrils. Silently he alerted the other animals. All together, they moved forward and rushed at the men.

"Help, I thought these were supposed to be gentle animals!" shouted the man who had watched Bambi.

In the dark and quiet the drumming of the deers' hooves was truly frightening. The first man quite forgot the trap he had fixed and as he ran, he caught his foot in his own snare and sprawled headlong. The wire bit deep into his ankle . . . Just before they reached him, the deer turned and galloped off into the darkness.

Safe among the trees, the deer slowed to a trot, then wandered off to find a more peaceful grazing spot.

A web in the bracken

An eagle was soaring high in the air, its great wings spread wide to catch the breeze. Far below, smaller birds were flying from branch to branch among the pine trees where red squirrels were feeding. Lower down still, roe deer grazed the forest floor and voles and shrews scuttled through the undergrowth.

At the tip of one pine tree's branch, swinging silently over the edge of a lake, was a fluffy, silken ball. It was an egg-sac, spun by a female spider around her eggs when she had laid them earlier in the year. She had left it swaying in the light winds with no sign of the thousand tiny eggs hidden inside their silken home.

The spring days warmed through the delicate shelter and the baby spiders hatched from their eggs and grew larger. At first they could not see or feed themselves. They had no poison in their fangs and were not yet able to spin silk for their own webs. They stayed in the egg-sac waiting.

They waited as the days grew warmer, and as they waited they shed the hard skeletons from around their soft bodies. New skeletons formed and the young spiders went on growing until the new skeletons had hardened too much for them to grow any more. When those had been shed too it was time for the spiders to leave the egg-sac. Now each could see out of its four eyes, and each had poison in its sharp fangs with which to kill any insects they could catch. Or any other spiders—even any of their 999 brothers and sisters! When the tight ball of tiny spiders split apart, they scattered quickly. Some of them just scuttled along the branch towards the trunk of the tree. Some went to left or right, along the short twigs to the very end where the year's new needles grew in bright green spiky clumps. Others spun their first wispy lines of thread and floated down on them in the breeze.

Even though they seemed so small and unimportant the forest was a dangerous place for them. The eagle which soared high above the trees did not notice them, and the roe deer in the bracken took no interest in them. But other creatures paid a lot of attention to the new arrivals. Some of the spiders that were floating on their silken threads were snapped up by birds, others ran along the branch straight to hungry ants and beetles. Some ate each other.

One of the spiders that had launched itself into mid-air went nearly all the way down to the lake before she landed on a leaf overhanging a rock. It was not a good place to start

a web, but she was luckier than she might have been. Only seconds before, a frog had leaped away from the rock and dropped with a plop into the calm water; if it had still been there when the spider had arrived it would have rolled out its long sticky tongue in a flash and eaten the spider there and then. But the frog was gone and the rock was safe.

The spider left its thread and started to look for a good place to make a web. She scurried away from the rock and into the forest. As she scrambled through the pine needles she passed what looked like a seven-legged spider, but it was the empty skeleton a male spider had outgrown and shed. He must have lost a leg somehow, but he would have grown a new one with his new skeleton. Adult males did not make webs, but if he was still nearby and hungry, the young spider would be in danger.

She carried on past the skeleton and scrambled up a stalk of bracken that grew close to the trunk of a tree. At last she had found a good place for a web. She spun a thread between the tip of the frond and the trunk of the tree, and when she had tightened it to make a bridge, she ran across it letting out a much looser thread underneath as she went. She climbed down into the middle of the second strand, and, spinning herself another, dropped down on it to a blade of grass. She fastened the third thread there and climbed back up it. On and on she went, spinning threads between the tree and the bracken and then round and round from the middle, weaving a strong thread out to the edge. Back she went to the middle. The thread was sticky but her own legs were oily and did not get caught in it.

At last she had finished. It was time for a rest, but she had hardly fastened the last thread when thump, a fat mosquito crashed into the new web. The spider had caught her first meal.

A place to sleep

The last rays of the sun faded from the wood and darkness crept in under the trees. There was a soft rustling in the dead leaves which lay thick on the woodland floor. A shrew scuttled about, twitching its long nose this way and that, in search of a big juicy earthworm to tug out of the ground and feed its constant hunger. Above the clearing, in the fork of a young tree, nestled a round, leafy ball, about the size of a grapefruit. Inside the skin of leaves was a neatly woven nest made of strips of honeysuckle bark. Inside this nest was a warm, furry, sandy coloured bundle. With his head tucked in and his eyes tight shut, slept a dormouse. It was dark outside in the wood now and the dormouse began to stir. Slowly he uncurled and stuck his head out through his leafy honeysuckle nest to see what the night had to offer. His large black eyes peered into the darkness. He lifted his whiskery nose to see what smells were carried on the air tonight. The sweet, strong scent of honeysuckle drifted up from the edge of the clearing.

The dormouse pushed out of the nest and scampered head first down the tree until he came to a familiar branch which hung out over the clearing. He ran right to the end of the branch, to where a tangled mass of honeysuckle straggled between his tree and the next. He crossed the honeysuckle bridge into a tall springy hazel bush. The honeysuckle had wrapped itself round the hazel twigs and it was here that the dormouse found the source of that wonderful smell – honeysuckle flowers. With his toes gripping tight around the thin branch, he hung upside down until he could just reach a bunch of flowers. He nibbled the bottom of one of the long yellow trumpets.

The wood rustled as the wind blew up and shook the branches of the trees. The dormouse heard the rain falling on the leaves high above before he felt the first drops. The next moment the heavens opened. All around him driving rain battered the leaves of the hazel bush and ran in tiny streams down the branches. The dormouse felt a wave of panic sweep over him. His first instinct was to run for his nest, but it was too far away. He would be soaked before he reached it. His soft thick fur was wonderful for keeping him warm when it was dry, but in the rain it soaked up the water like a sponge, chilling him to the bone.

The nearest shelter was an empty wooden box which had been nailed to the trunk of a nearby ash tree. In there he would be safe. He ran back along the branch and into the heart of the hazel bush and then up the tallest of its thin trunks. This one leaned against the trunk of the ash tree and he scrambled from hazel to ash, then up the trunk until he reached the wooden box. He climbed onto the roof of the box, reached over the front and disappeared head first into a small round hole.

Inside the box, it was dry, but the dormouse was cold and wet. He looked even smaller now as his damp fur clung to his back. Outside, the rain lashed the sides of the box and the tree shuddered and creaked in the wind. The dormouse huddled in the corner of the box while the storm raged on.

All night he could hear the rain dripping through the trees. He was hungry now and very tired. What could he do? It was too wet out there to find food and if he tried he would probably die from the cold and hunger. So the dormouse did what he knew how to do best: he went to sleep. For three days and nights he stayed curled up in the wooden box, hardly breathing, his sleep was so deep. Outside it rained.

On the fourth day something was different. The sun shone on a dazzling fresh wood, cleaned by the storm. The leaves all around steamed as the hot rays of the sun dried away the rain. The sun fell on the box and the warmth around him stirred the dormouse in his sleep. And when evening came he finally awoke and peered out of the box again. He sniffed the fresh evening air and a new smell reached him. He climbed out of the box and made his way through the branches to the wayfaring tree. He followed his nose to the end of the branch. Hanging below the soft downy leaves was a bunch of berries. His nose had not been wrong. The rain and the sun had ripened the first fruit.

The dormouse reached down into the bunch of berries and nibbled on the ripe black fruit. He still felt hungry and tired but he knew now that autumn was coming and – if the weather held and the rain kept off – he would be alright.

The owl's windy night

Deep in the heart of the forest the old trees creaked and groaned even in the lightest wind, and where the young trees grew close together their branches often squeaked as they rubbed against each other. The forest was old. It was much smaller now than it had once been, but it still covered mile after mile of hills and ridges, dropped into valleys and hid tumbling rivers. Here and there were clearings where in summer, sunlight fell down onto small lakes and sparkled on their still waters. At other times, rain fell on them in big splashing drops, and wind ruffled small grey waves from one end to the other.

The tawny owl was used to all the sights and sounds of the forest. She had been born there and now lived in a hole in the trunk of a tree that stood on its highest ridge. She had raised three chicks there. Three silly looking, fluffy things that had chipped their way out of their round white eggs with their egg teeth and started to demand food. It had seemed ages before they could fly; they had sidled up and down the branch outside the nest calling all the time for more to eat.

But now they were grown up and able to hunt for themselves, swooping softly down on silent wings to catch their prey. The downy fluff had been replaced by beautiful, sleek, mottled feathers. Her daughter was almost grey, but her two sons were almost chestnut in colour and they all had great big black eyes, just like her own.

The three young owls had left the nest and found homes of their own, but they were not far off: she often heard them calling as she flew on her nightly hunting round. "Keuwick!" "Kewick!" "Koowick!" Three very slightly different calls as they sat on their perches watching and listening for the tiny movements of an unwary woodmouse or bank vole. Like her, they had several favourite perches around their hunting grounds. Even when they were hunting a long way off she could hear the tremble of their strong voices hooo . . . hoo . . . huhooing through the trees.

She had heard them that night, but even with her excellent hearing it was harder than usual to catch the sound of their voices or the tiny sounds of dry bracken being brushed over pine needles as a mouse scrabbled for a fallen berry. The wind had been growing stronger all through the afternoon, and by the time darkness came and the owls were ready to begin hunting, the treetops were lurching backwards and forwards. Their branches swayed across the

sky, sweeping across the silver face of the moon when it shone out briefly between the racing clouds.

At first it was still possible to hunt because in the very middle of the forest the wind did not disturb the heavy lower branches very much. And although it was impossible to hear well with so much creaking and wheezing going on, the owl's big round eyes were as sharp as ever. Then suddenly the wind began to tear at the trees with terrific force. It snapped and cracked great branches and trunks as though they were the smallest twigs, and even wrenched whole trees from the earth, scattering them carelessly across the ground.

Frightened, the owl flew out of the way of the wind. She perched, blinking, on an old mossy log that had fallen under the shelter of a rocky overhang. The terrible rush of wind died down as quickly as it had come, and after that the rest of the stormy night seemed almost peaceful.

By the time the first streaks of light appeared, not even a gentle breeze was left to disturb the trees' branches. The owl was hungry. She had not had a good night's hunting, but it was time to return to her nest. She spread her broad wings and flapped gently back through the forest lowlands and up towards her ridge.

Her nest was gone! Her tree was gone! Torn down by the wind and rolled aside. She glided hopelessly for a while around the fallen tree. Eventually she flew back down into the forest to roost on a branch. Hungry and homeless she slept there all day, ignoring the small frightened birds that flocked around her chattering angrily. In spite of their efforts to make her leave, she did not go until dusk. By then she was hungrier than ever, but most especially she was anxious to find a safe and comfortable new hole . . . in a good strong tree.

The hunter

Weasels learn to hunt as a game with their brothers and sisters. But it was not a game now. It was time to develop skills, to find escape paths for times of danger, and to search out the secrets of the land. Being a good hunter would make the difference between life and death. The young weasel moved between the tree roots and bracken stems. Just a few days ago, he had been living with other weasel kittens. Now he was on his own and he needed to find his own food. If he did not catch anything, he would starve.

There were rabbits living nearby, where the woodland bordered a farm. A group of them were cropping the grass and he moved silently towards them. But they were too big – all fully grown. He had never caught a rabbit before. A young one would be easiest. He turned towards the stream which ran down the slope to the ruins of an old house. Once, the stream had provided water for the people living there. Now it just trickled through the ruins, running down to the edge of the cliffs where it dropped to the sea.

The young weasel edged his way through the ferns and meadowsweet to check the stream. He was learning to ignore the scent of the late summer flowers, to seek out the scent of food. A faint smell lingered on the bank. A grey wagtail disturbed the water and, beyond it, a nervous vole moved towards its nest under an old tree stump. It would have to pass the weasel on its way. The weasel waited, only his eyes moving. The vole paused for a moment, its shape not quite hidden by some tufts of grass. The weasel was hungry. He pounced. The vole leaped down the muddy bank – and slipped. The weasel had found his supper.

When he had finished eating, the weasel returned to his burrow below one of the stunted oak trees near the ruins. Living near the ruins was good – and bad. The fallen walls and rotting beams were home to rats and mice, beetles and bugs – all good weasel food. But the one high corner of the building still standing sheltered a family of barn owls who enjoyed weasel for supper.

He took care when he left his burrow that evening, sniffing the air for clues to food, and for clues to danger. He slid his narrow body between the stones and tree roots, towards the rabbits' feeding place. He could see a mixed group of young and old rabbits. But the breeze was in a bad direction, blowing his scent towards them.

He found a good hiding place between the roots of an old elder bush, then sat up on his haunches to take a better look. If he was quick, he might be lucky. Suddenly, the breeze blew stronger. A young rabbit turned round and the weasel leaped towards it. Too late. His scent had reached the rabbits and he was too far away. They disappeared down their well-worn path through the grass.

The weasel turned towards the stream. There was not even a vole in sight. But another scent drifted towards him. He followed it back to its source, the narrow tunnel of a shrew. The tunnel was empty.

He moved on to the ruins. It was dusk now and he would need to watch out for the barn owls. He stopped near the fallen walls, listening for interesting squeaks and scratchings, sniffing for scents. Before long, he heard mice not far away. He edged forwards, whiskers twitching. Suddenly a shadow fell across the stones, and a pale, gliding shape drifted into view, feathered legs and long talons hanging down. The owl dropped to the ground, then rose swiftly with a mouse in its claws. The other frightened mice ran away, one straight to the weasel. He caught it gratefully. It was small but he was hungry.

Towards dawn, he headed for the rabbits' burrows again and waited in the hedgerow for them to come out to feed. This time the breeze was from a different direction and the rabbits could not smell him. A few of the younger rabbits began to wander further from the group. One careless young rabbit moved nearer to the hedgerow. The weasel sank back into the damp leaves, watching, waiting . . . A little nearer it came, then nearer still. The weasel pounced. He needed all his strength to hold on but little by little, the young rabbit weakened. At last the weasel dragged it away to a hollow under a fallen tree.

As the first autumn leaves began to fall around him, and new scents drifted through the wood, the weasel ate his fill. He had become a hunter. He would survive.

The flying squirrel

Gripping the twigs tightly with her tiny fists, Flick looked like the highest squirrel in the world. Up and down she swung, up and down in the topmost branches of the great beech tree which was as breathtaking as the Big Wheel at a funfair. She could look down over the whole wood. Flick knew all the trees by the games she played in them. She and her brother loved to chase along the branches from tree to tree—bouncing in the willow, spring-springing through the ash tree, hide-and-seeking in the dark hollows of the oak, swing-swaying up the birch twigs and slip-sliding down the beech trunk's helter-skelter.

Where was her brother now? She peered down through the tangle of branches. Was he hiding? Far below her Flick saw the ripple of a silvery tail as Dart came bounding lightly over the ground. With nimble, elastic ease he scampered up to the shoulder of the first branch with a hazelnut in his mouth. Dart had found the first nut of the autumn. He sat up, his tail a fluffy question mark. Then holding the large end of the nut tightly in his paws, he cracked it with his teeth to get at the sweet bit inside.

When Flick saw the nut, she gave a squeak of excitement. Her first instinct was to chase him for it! But then she stretched up from her high lookout and was able to spy all the hazelnut bushes around. Clusters of nuts were beginning to show, fat and ripe through the leaves.

Flick's teeth made an excited chattering as she looked for a way to reach them without having to go past Dart, and without touching the ground.

Dart heard her call, so he dropped the nutshell and hid behind the tree. He became like a small grey stick, growing from the trunk, not a whisker moved, his claws held tight, his bright eyes alert. He could hear Flick creeping down to a lower branch. She was trying to get to the hazel bushes, testing to see which was the longest branch, the one that would reach across to them. Dart decided to chase her. He flew up the far side of the tree and spiralled down till he was above Flick. Down he came now, on a switch-back bough to surprise her. The chase began!

Away they went at high speed, bounding through the beech tree. Up and up and up, twisting and turning like trapeze acrobats. Flick tried every trick she knew, zig-zagging away and turning suddenly. Round and round the trunk

and down. Round and round again and up! Dart followed Flick everywhere she went, faster and faster. Flick and Dart, their tails like silver plumes, leaped from branch to branch.

Then bounding up a long thin bough, not knowing which way to turn, Flick suddenly stopped. Dart who was close behind collided into her. Like clowns on a tightrope they bumped together and overbalanced. Dart tumbled, over and over, down to a soft landing in the leaves! Flick just managed to hold on to the branch, which swayed wildly. Dart was unharmed. He was having a quick groom, rubbing his face and straightening the fur of his tail.

Slowly Flick recovered and balanced her way to the very end of the long bough. This was the one that she had been looking for. It was the one that stretched out towards the hazelnut bushes. There were the nuts, hanging in clusters but they were still too far away for an ordinary jump.

Dart glanced up when twigs and leaves began to fall around him. He could see Flick biting off all the little sticks that grew along the branch. She seemed to be making a runway. He watched as she turned to size up the distance and to check that it was all clear. Then with a flick of her tail she raced at full speed along the branch and catapulted off the end. It was a wonderful sight! Like a ballet dancer, she seemed to float in the air for a long time and then with a crash of leaves she landed among the hazelnuts.

Dart raced to join her. They were both very hungry after their games and sat feasting on the nuts till they could eat no more. Flick picked one more nut and carried it in her mouth to the ground. She found a clear space under a tree and scratched out a hole. She put the nut in and covered it up and patted the earth down to hide it.

Dart did the same. He poked his in with his nose and swept the leaves over it with his paws. They made a store of nuts for winter. Then tired out, they clambered up the tree and went to sleep curled under their bushy tails.

Fur and feathers

As they finished their day's work, the farmers were not aware of the pair of eyes high above them on the hillside. While they put away their tools and machines, they thought about supper and tomorrow's tasks. But all the time something was watching them closely from the patch of woodland in the hollow where the stream began its journey to the fields below. In the fading evening light, the wildcat followed their movements.

The autumn air was growing cold. Her kittens had finished sunning themselves on the nearby rocks. Now they were home in their nest, hungry and waiting. They would be together for only a few more weeks before they left to find homes of their own and to hunt for themselves. For now, they could enjoy the taste of the food their mother provided. Last night they had eaten mountain hare. What would she find for them tonight?

She knew every rock and every tree around their home. Sometimes at dawn, sometimes at dusk, she had searched out all the food she could find there. But she was not the only one looking for food. The buzzards nesting amongst the jagged rocks at the top of the hill searched too. And they liked mountain hare. As they soared above the trees, they could often see things the wildcat missed.

Tonight, the breeze brought few interesting scents. As evening came, she left the trees, moving cautiously down through the heather and bracken on the slopes below. Among the plants, her pale golden fur, spotted with grey, hardly showed. Even her ringed tail slid unseen between the stalks as she crept silently along.

Most of the humans were now inside their buildings. But they might not lock up their chickens till later. A farm chicken would do well for her family. Along the way, she sniffed the air. A pheasant would save her the risky visit to a farm. But there were none about.

Ahead of her, a few lights came on in the windows of the farmhouses, and cars brought people home from work to the village beyond. She followed the bank of the stream towards the nearest farm.

As she crept through a garden towards the yard, a heap of oozy kitchen rubbish gave off some interesting smells. There were probably a few bones and some leftover meat scraps amongst the rotting peelings. Keeping low to the ground, she moved around the heap, watchful.

Behind the barn, the farmer was removing a broken part from his tractor. His wife was making supper, putting the vegetable peelings into a bucket to take to the heap.

From somewhere ahead of the wildcat came the scent of live chicken. She sniffed, moving through the shadows towards it. It came from an old wooden shed where a sick chicken had been left for the day and forgotten. The rickety door was still open, and the farmyard was empty. The chicken looked like a straggly pile of feathers on the earth floor. As it raised its head, it only saw the shining eyes before the wildcat pounced.

The chicken was hers but her movement had caught the door and it swung closed, trapping her tail. She howled loudly, bringing the farmer from his work on the tractor.

"What was that?" his wife asked as he passed the kitchen window.

"Sounds like old Sampson shut in the shed," he replied. When he reached the shed, he lifted the latch on the door, thinking his old farm cat was trapped inside. But instead, a hissing, spitting blur of fur and feathers shot past him, through the yard, under the wire fence, and away.

His wife appeared, carrying a bowl of milk for Sampson. "Is he all right?" she asked.

"That was never Sampson," he said. "More likely one of those wildcats from the wood. We've lost that chicken."

While Sampson came padding round the corner of the barn, the wildcat began climbing the hill. Her tail still stung but she had found food for the family. Next time, though, she would have to look elsewhere.

As she crossed the stream, the cool water soothed her sore tail. She threaded her way through the heather and bracken, then climbed the familiar rocks and headed towards the nest among the trees.

A few minutes later, she was safe below the fallen birch tree, sharing the food with her kittens.

A new home for the fox

It was autumn. A beam of sunlight shone down through the branches onto a pile of brown and orange leaves at the foot of a tree.

Curled up in the middle of the pile, enjoying the warmth, was a dog fox. He was almost fully grown and the greyish fuzz of his fur had changed to a smooth russet colour that made him almost invisible among the autumn leaves. Another leaf fell from the tree and dropped onto his nose. His eyes opened in a flash. His whole body stiffened, and then relaxed when he realized there was no danger. Still, he was awake now. He yawned and rubbed his paw roughly across his face. Then, without making a sound, he stood up and sniffed the air. Evening was coming – it was nearly time to be off.

Tonight he was going to start looking for a new home. He had been born in the wood that spring, in an earth only a few yards away from his pile of leaves. It was a good place for foxes to live, but now that his family was so big there was not really enough food for everyone. Either they would all have to eat less, or some of them must find new homes where there were no other foxes around.

He had been getting ready for his journey. For several nights he had explored new paths through the wood, paths which led to places he had never been before. Now the time had come to choose the best direction. He looked around quickly and then slipped quietly away, heading for the edge of the wood.

The other day he had caught more mice than he could eat and he had hidden them under a root of an oak tree.

The hiding place was not quite on his way, but now was a good time to eat them. He turned off his path and darted under a hawthorn bush and through a patch of bracken to the hollow where the oak tree stood. As he drew near the tree, he began to feel nervous. Was anything watching where he was going? Foxes never trust anyone near their food. He stopped still at the top of the hollow and, dropping down into the bracken, inched his way forward. His ears were pricked up to hear the slightest sound, his black nose twitched to catch the scent of another fox, and his eyes flicked from side to side. There was no-one around. Keeping close to the ground he slipped quickly and quietly into the hollow. He scrabbled at the leaves and loose earth under which he had hidden the mice. All the time he was eating

he was on the look out, and as soon as he had finished he ran straight back to the path and out of the wood.

He travelled quite a long way that night. To be safe he kept to the edge of the wood. It would have been faster to go in a straight line across the fields, but it was more dangerous, too. When daylight came he found a place to rest in an empty badger's sett. It was his first night away from home.

The next evening, when he set off again, he felt a little braver and he left the edge of the wood and headed downhill along the hedgerow. He had not gone far, though, before he began to smell dogs. At first the scent was weak, as if they had not been that way for some time, so he trotted on carefully. After a while, though, the smell became stronger and he knew that there had been dogs around just a short time ago. They might come back at any moment. He was very frightened now and began to back away. In the shelter of the thickest part of the hedge he stood shivering a little as the sound of three barking dogs drifted up the hill from a farmyard. This was not a good place. He'd come the wrong way. Suddenly he turned and ran, racing back to the shelter of the wood.

When he had got his breath back he stopped to look around. Somehow he had run to a part of the wood that he had not visited before. He sniffed. No dogs here. No foxes either. Maybe he had been lucky after all. He nibbled at the blackberries on a nearby bramble and forgot about being frightened. What could he smell? The scent of rabbits was strong all around and he could smell mice too, and pheasants. He trotted on, sniffing out the secrets of the place. By the time dawn came his stomach was full and he was ready to curl up in an empty rabbit burrow. Tomorrow he would make it bigger and more comfortable – by accident he had found his new home.

The woodmouse's secret

On the wide shelf of a flat brown fungus sat a woodmouse. The fungus stuck out from the bottom of the tree trunk like half an upside-down dinner plate. The woodmouse's strong back legs and big feet supported him, while his long tail, with the end hanging over the edge of his platform, acted as a balance. In his front paws he carefully held a large grass seed. He delicately turned the seed in his paws, carefully nibbling into the sweet, soft centre, and letting the dry papery husk drop to the ground. His large ears listened intently for any unusual sounds from the rustling, murmuring wood. His big black eyes searched the darkness around him as every now and again he stopped eating to check that all was still safe.

When he had finished his seed, the mouse leaped from his perch and landed with barely a sound on the damp brown leaves. A few bounds from his long back legs and he had reached the hazel bush. He scampered up into the lower branches and then ran to the end where nuts hung in pairs beneath the leaves. The nuts were large and ripe, but the shells were still soft and green, easier to break than the hard brown cases which would litter the ground in a few weeks' time. The mouse balanced on the branch and bit his way through the stalk of a nut. Holding it firmly with his teeth he jumped down and started to nibble a neat round hole in the shell, so he could reach the sweet fruit inside. Soon there was a small pile of empty shells beneath the bush.

Feeling rather full now, the mouse began to store a few nuts for later. He bit firmly into another soft shell and then bounded off with it to an old oak tree. The trunk spread out at the bottom, with the thick arms of its roots reaching from its base, hugging the leafy floor before disappearing underground. The mouse disappeared into a small hole in the mossy carpet at the base of the tree. The hole led to a complicated network of tunnels, dug into the earth between the tree roots. The mouse pattered along the tunnels until he reached a slightly wider chamber. Something had been there before for there was already a pile of nuts on the floor. He dropped his nut into the heap. Over the next few months, while the wood was full of nuts and berries and the rich pickings of autumn, he would add to his treasure trove – and perhaps start a few more secret stores. He would need this for the winter.

He hurried off along another passage and out into the air again. His large black eyes searched around to make sure all was still safe. The mouse shared the woodland floor with many other animals. There were the voles, of course, with their blunt noses and short little legs and tails. He usually ignored or avoided them as they bustled about their business. Then there were the shrews, who never seemed to keep still. They were always whiffling around under the surface of the leaf litter, sniffing out insects with their long twitching noses, wrestling with earthworms almost as large as themselves. The shrews didn't bother the mouse either. What really frightened him were the long thin weasels. They hunted on the ground, climbed the trees to raid the birds' nests and, worst of all, even managed to squeeze their slender bodies down the wider burrows of the mice.

But tonight weasels were not the problem. The mouse sat still as his large ears caught the sound of something close by on the other side of the tree. The next moment another pair of round black eyes was staring straight at him as a fully grown male mouse approached. The woodmouse was still young, and no match for this large heavy stranger. Before he had time to react, the newcomer flew at him with a fury of teeth and scrabbling paws. For a few seconds they fought in a spinning squeaking mass, then the younger woodmouse broke free and fled for his life.

For a few seconds more the big stranger followed close behind him as they ran across the damp leaves; then he was alone again. At last he came to a hollow branch that lay half hidden in the leaves. He shot inside. He felt battered and sore, but no real damage was done. And he had lost his store of nuts – but then perhaps it had been too good to be true, to find that well dug empty burrow, with a little collection of food already in place. Of course, the true owner was bound to return. But things could have been worse; the air was warm, the weasels were hunting somewhere else tonight and there were plenty more nuts on the trees.

Winter's on the way

As long as anyone could remember, jays had lived in the old woods above the cliffs. Their shrieks could be heard from the tiny beaches that filled the bays and from the narrow road that threaded its way through the trees at the edge of the woods. Few holidaymakers used the bumpy cliff road, and the jays were usually left in peace. Now it was autumn, a quiet time for holidaymakers, a busy time for jays. While the few people who passed that way looked anxiously at the long drop to the sea, the jays darted about, taking short cuts across the cliffs, or flying through the trees in search of acorns.

Today, only one car was making its way along the cliffs. The driver was not used to this kind of road and while the jays went about their autumn tasks, he decided to stop and rest. The family spread a rug on the ground beside the trees, where rhododendrons and brambles provided some shelter, and began setting out their food. An angry jay shrieked off to join some others, its loud "skaak-skaak" echoing through the trees.

"What a noisy bird!" one of the children remarked.

"Not as bad as you," his mother replied.

They could hear jays in other parts of the wood, and away from the picnic place birds were still flying about or hopping along the ground. Unless the jays now worked hard, they would not survive the winter. The family, enjoying a picnic of scones and homemade jam, had no idea that they were interrupting one jay's important work: they were sitting on one of his food stores. That was why he had shrieked off when they arrived. He had carefully collected five acorns, and had found a perfect place to store the first one when these people had come and sat down right on top of the loose stone. He watched them from a tall tree. Perhaps they would soon leave. Fortunately, they did.

As soon as the sound of their car faded into the distance, the jay came back to check the stone. It had been pressed firmly into the ground but he soon loosened it, buried one of his acorns, and found places for the others. Now he would continue.

Some he hid under leaves and roots, others under stones or below rocky ledges. If he could not find a suitable place, he sometimes dug a hole in the ground with his beak. Most of the hiding places were close together, among the trees, but yesterday he had flown half a mile along the cliffs,

carrying several acorns in his wide throat. He could carry up to eight at a time!

The jay hid most of the nuts he found but now and then he stopped to eat one or two. He held them carefully between his toes and pulled off the shell, eating the middle.

All through September and October the jay worked until by the time the acorn season was over and the trees were bare, he had hidden about two thousand acorns. Last year he had been able to find his hidden supplies even when the snow came and covered the ground. This year he was a strong, full-grown bird. He would need plenty of food.

Winter would bring other changes. All year round, he had to preen and oil his feathers. In summer, he splashed in puddles as well. But now the puddles were frozen. Instead, he looked for an ants' nest where he crouched amongst the ants, his shiny blue-edged wings outstretched, getting rid of any tiny insects that were stuck to his feathers.

The snow started to fall one night in early January. At first, there were just tiny dots, blown in the wind, but by morning they had become large flakes which lay on the ground and edged the branches with a furry white coating. The birds huddled in the trees, fluffing out their feathers to keep themselves warm. It was for such times as this that the jays hid their acorns. The jay looked around him. The snow covered many clues to hiding places, and it was still too early in the year for any acorns to send up shoots.
A few birds set off and scratched about for some time before they found food. Others stayed in the shelter of the trees.

He headed for the picnic place. There were no tracks from other birds, and the shape of his stone could still be seen through the thin layer of snow. He gripped a corner of the stone in his beak, pulling it upwards to loosen the ice that fixed it to the ground. The acorn was safe below. It was just a small amount of food but it was enough to prepare him for his search. There were more acorns nearby.

New arrivals

It was the time of year when nearly every morning was foggy. It was always worse on one side of the valley than the other, and the rooks seemed to prefer the foggier side. Towards the top of the field where cows grazed in the summer was a copse. It had been there for hundreds of years, never any bigger or any smaller than it was now. Trees had fallen and new ones had grown up. Some had simply carried on standing there from the beginning and creaked and groaned in the storms at the year's end. And all the time the copse had been there the rooks had been there too. Generations of them had built their homes high in the swaying branches.

In the summer they flew down to plod pompously among the grazing cattle or sit in groups on that part of the old fence where the creamy white flowers grew thickest. But the lazy warm days were over for the year. The cows had been taken in for the winter and now the field belonged only to the rooks. They were not much bothered by the cold.

The heavy flapping of their wings seemed to fill the air in the early foggy mornings as they dropped down from their nests to dig around in the cold ground for earthworms and leatherjackets. At this time of year there were acorns to be found, too, lying under the oak trees at the far end of the field where the fog was thickest.

Everything disappeared until the feeble winter sun warmed the cold white air and cleared it again. Even the biggest trees were just like shadows, and down on the wet grass the rooks were almost invisible. But they could still be heard. Their harsh, croaking "kaaghs" echoed around the valley and up into the woods as they called to each other.

There were hundreds of them living in the rookery now. Their shaggy black nests filled the tops of the trees. They were always together. They ate together and they played together – most of them did. They seemed to like inventing games and playing tricks, but sometimes the younger rooks went too far. That year the games of six young rooks had been too rough and the older birds had chased them away to live apart from the main rookery. They had taken over nests in the wood at the edge of the field. Over the years many rooks had spent time there before being allowed back into the copse.

So, for a while, when all the other rooks had flapped down into the field or flown wheeling through the air, the six had not been welcome. Sometimes they would try flying over to join the others. At first the flock took no notice of them but before long they would do something to make themselves unpopular and then they would be chased away again. They were always searching for something to do and sometimes it seemed as if they could not help being annoying.

One morning there was no fog, but it was very cold. The rooks had fluffed up their feathers to keep warm, so that they looked as if they had baggy trousers on their legs. The six young rooks were sitting in a line on a branch of their tree trying to push each other off. Nothing very much had happened to interest them, and they were about to fly over the field to drop twigs on some of the older rooks when they saw something black creeping across the sky. The shape grew in size and came closer and closer until they could make out what it was. It was rooks: hundreds of rooks, maybe a thousand. The air was filled with the slap, flap of their wings as they circled the woodland and fields. And then they began to land.

The six young rooks had never seen anything like it. They were not yet a year old—they still had feathers around their beaks to prove it. To them the rookery had always seemed a quiet place. But the older birds had seen it all before. Every winter rooks flew in from the east and roosted with them in the valley. Some came all the way from Russia.

The young rooks flew down to take a look. There were rooks everywhere: rooks on the ground, rooks in trees, rooks on fences—and all of them hungry. Other birds might have fought strangers who came to eat on their land, but not the sociable rooks. The rooks from the east could share whatever they could find. But the six young birds called loudly to one another. Here were a thousand unsuspecting newcomers to play their tricks on through the winter. With perfect aim they dropped their first twigs.

Just a meal of corn

As the year came to an end, a cold wind blew from the north. The puddles froze over, and snow began to fall. It drifted between the trees at the corner of the field, where the pheasants roosted at night. When dawn came after the long snowfall, the ground was hard, and clues to food had disappeared. The pheasants sheltered deep among the fallen leaves below the brambles.

The first pheasant to move about could be seen clearly against the white background. Her light and dark brown feathers had been useful when she wanted to hide amongst the leaves. Now they showed up against the smooth white drifts. But hunger kept her searching for food, and she moved further and further from the safety of the brambles. She had eaten only a shrivelled berry and a thin worm. She needed more.

A fox's tracks lay ahead in the snow but he had passed by in the night. The wind was already filling his footprints with drifting snow. The pheasant crossed his path, making her way to the hedgerow that bordered the far side of the field. It would provide shelter and camouflage, and maybe some food. As she edged her way between the roots and stems, little showers of snow fell from the twigs above. But where the hedge was thickest, there were patches of bare earth. She scratched about but found little.

Across the field, she heard several pheasants calling from the trees at the edge of the wood. Something had disturbed them. Silence soon returned, and a small group of pheasants gave up searching in the field and flew towards the others.

Soon, the noise began again. It was the farmer, his boots cracking ice on the puddles as he walked along. He had brought his sheep some extra food and he wanted to see how hard the ground had frozen. He completed his tasks and then turned back to the farmhouse. He looked across the field, where the pheasant lay hidden in the hedge. But he was thinking about his sheep and looked up at the big dark clouds bringing more snow.

The pheasant moved on. She found a few berries but it was a long search. As the morning passed, she reached the curve of the hedge that led to the wood. She flew across the corner of the field to take a closer look. Snow covered the ground in the wood but scattered about on it were little heaps of corn. She stopped beside the first one and ate all she could. Then she moved on, searching for signs of food she might need later. There were several other pheasants nearby. They had found the piles of corn but none of them seemed to be searching for any other food.

More snow began to fall. She sheltered amongst the leaves that had collected below a group of tree roots. It was a dry, comfortable place and she stayed there until nightfall. At dusk, she flew up into the branches to roost, safely out of reach of any prowling fox.

The air was cold. Now and then, a few snowflakes found their way between the branches above her. An owl was searching for his supper at the edge of the wood. The snow made it easier for him to spot movements across the ground. A patch of fallen leaves, free of snow, rustled then settled. It might just be the breeze, or it might be a shrew hiding from the owl.

Next day, as the pheasant began her usual search for food, she heard the unwelcome sounds of a man's voice and a dog's bark. She returned to the tree roots, watching carefully. The sounds drew nearer. First the dog passed by, on his way to disturb a group of magpies. Then the man walked past. As he did so, he scattered handfuls of corn.

Before long, pheasants appeared from below the leaves and bushes to enjoy the feast. There were several males. Their blue-green heads and red wattles showed up brightly against the snow. But they didn't seem specially watchful, and wandered about taking corn from here and there. Soon, most of the corn had gone. Only their tracks showed where they had found it.

This was an easy way to survive bad weather. The pheasant looked about her, then joined the others. Several days passed by with no dangers except a hungry weasel who found a vole, and a falling branch unable to hold the weight of the snow. The man and the dog walked through the wood each morning leaving a trail of corn. More snow fell but still the corn was provided.

Then a day came when more men and more dogs entered the wood. The dogs ran about barking and the men began hitting the bushes with sticks, shouting, and rustling the leaves about. They wanted the pheasants to move. But why? Those birds who hid below the brambles, or amongst the leaves, suddenly found everything crashing down around them. Branches snapped, twigs were crushed into the ground, leaves were torn from their stems. The men and dogs forced pathways through the undergrowth, breaking or parting anything that blocked their way. But the pheasant below the tree roots moved deeper into her earthy hollow. She would try to wait till the danger passed.

A stick hit the roots above her but she kept still. Some loose earth fell around her but she made no movement. The men passed by, still shouting and stamping about. A few pheasants tried to escape by running deeper into the wood. Others flew out of the trees across the field. As they did so, a worse noise began. Loud bangs disturbed the morning air, while here and there a pheasant dropped to the ground. As it did so, a dog ran out to collect it.

All morning, the shouting and noise continued. Then, the men and dogs began to leave the wood. Corn lay trampled in the earth, bushes and brambles lay twisted and broken. A few pheasants came out to look around them but below a tree root, one pheasant lay still and silent. She had not been hurt, and she had not yet moved. She would wait a little longer, hungry or not.

As the sun began to set, she came out to look for food to help her through the night. She dug some corn out of the mud and ate well. Then she returned to her tree.

She was going to stay in the wood. There was plenty of food. The men might return. If they did, she would stay amongst her tree roots. She would let them feed her but she would give them no clue to her hiding place.

The wood at night

A harvest moon rose over the wood, huge and yellow as it began its slow nightly journey across the autumn sky.

A few hours before, the wood had been a patchwork of red, gold, brown and green, but these colours now faded into shades of black and grey. Over the last week the woodland floor had been thickening with a new carpet of crunchy leaves, lying in drifts and piles over last year's damp leaf mould. At the base of a large oak tree one of these piles of leaves rustled and heaved. The branches above were still, so it was not the wind that was causing the commotion. The pile of leaves was noisy, too, not just with crunching and crackling, but with sniffing and snorting. Between the roots of the tree, under the leaves, a hedgehog was making his winter nest.

High above in the tree a squirrel slept curled in her twiggy drey in a fork of the tree. Higher still, a patch of thick knobbly bark had lifted away from the trunk of the tree, where a storm from the year before had torn off one of the branches. The gap between the trunk and the bark was narrow, but large enough for the little pipistrelle bat that had squeezed herself into the crevice.

The sun had not been down for long and the air in the wood still held some of the heat from the sunny autumn day. A small cloud of midges was dancing over the pond and the long-legged crane-flies flew and crawled in the grass around the water's edge. The little pipistrelle squeezed out of her hiding place behind the bark, spread her wings and flew off towards the pond to hunt for midges before the night cooled down. In another week or so the night would be too cold for insects. She had to try and fatten up quickly before cold and lack of food forced her into her long winter sleep.

The moon rose higher and a pale silvery light filled the woodland clearing. As a cloud drifted slowly across the moon its inky black shadow gently swallowed the shadows of the trees, until the whole wood was cast into a deeper shade of black. Under cover of the darkness a badger was collecting bedding for its sett. She had gathered up a large bundle of dry bracken and grass from the edge of the clearing and was now pulling it all back to her underground tunnels. There was a definite knack to collecting bedding; she held her bundle of bracken and grass tightly in place with her chin and forepaws, at the same time shuffling rapidly backwards towards the entrance to the sett.

At the other side of the clearing a large dog fox was busy sniffing at something on the ground. A scattered pile of grey feathers was all that remained of a plump pigeon that he'd managed to catch unawares the previous day. He chewed briefly on one of the feathers before losing interest and trotting over to a bramble bush nearby. He spent several minutes at the bush, nibbling at the remains of the over-ripe berries which still hung from the prickly stems. When the fox had gone, disappearing back into the undergrowth in search of mice and voles, the clearing was quiet again.

At the edge of the wood a few pale moths fluttered under the branches of the trees. Among them there was also a larger shape dipping and weaving between the branches. This was a long-eared bat. Like the little pipistrelle she was taking advantage of this warm late autumn night to hunt and feed on the insects. Her broad wings helped her to twist and turn under the branches. At times she seemed to hover in one place before circling around the trunk again.
Her huge ears were picking up the tiniest sounds the moths made. She could even hear them vibrating their wings as they perched on the leaves, warming up ready for flight. The

bat had already caught a large number of smaller insects. She ate these rapidly as she hunted but the moth she now had in her mouth was too big for that. Holding it firmly with her sharp little teeth she flew to the next door tree and with a neat twist of her body, landed upside down on a low branch. Here she could hang on safely with her feet and concentrate on finishing off the juicy moth. Under the branch was a small pile of moth wings: this was obviously one of her favourite feeding perches.

On the other side of the tree a tawny owl sat higher in the branches, peering into the wood with his large eyes. His head swivelled almost full circle as he caught a faint sound

and movement below, at the very edge of his senses. His mournful "hooo, hooo, hoo-oo" call was answered from deeper in the wood by the sharper "kee-wick" of another tawny owl. The owl ruffled his feathers, leaned forward and then launched himself into the air, slowly gliding down through the dark wood on his silent wings.

As winter drew closer, days and nights of frost, snow, wind and rain lay in waiting. But tonight, on one of the last warm nights of the autumn, the many different woodland animals hunted, scavenged, built their nests, collected their bedding and made sure that they were ready for the long cold winter ahead.

Something to think about

All the things that happen to the animals in this book happen to real animals every day. Every day, one creature or another has to find a new home, to challenge its own kind for food or shelter, to escape from larger animals who hunt it for food, or to become a hunter itself, to find food for itself and its family.

The plants and animals in any wood depend on one another in a hundred different ways. Trees provide shelter, both in their branches and down among their roots; grass, leaves and fruit provide food; insects carry pollen from flower to flower; birds and animals spread seeds so that new plants can grow.

The different kinds of animals depend on each other as well. There are many that eat only plants but there are others, both large and small, that use other animals for at least part of their food. One thing you will not find is any animal being needlessly cruel to another, whether it belongs to its own species or to a different one. It is very rare for an animal to hunt unless it is hungry or has a hungry family to feed. And if there is a fight over space or a mate, it usually ends before the loser is seriously hurt.

In most of the stories in this book, the animals are successful. They *do* find new homes; they *do* escape their enemies; they *do* learn to forage and hunt when they need to. But even in the most peaceful woodland there is danger for animals on every side. People often make it more dangerous for the animals that live there. Next time you walk through a wood, remember that it's home for countless small, unseen creatures . . . so please, tread carefully.